Published by West Midlands History Limited

Minerva Mill Innovation Centre, Alcester, Warwickshire, UK.

All photographic images are © Birmingham Museums Trust except p.21 © Paul Binns and

p.7 © Staffordshire County Council.

The rights of Cathy Shingler and Neil Max Emmanuel to be identified as author and illustrator of this work have been

asserted by them in accordance with the Copyright, Designs and Patents Act 1988.

ISBN: 978-1-905036-27-1

SAXON GOLD

Cathy Shingler
Neil Max Emmanuel

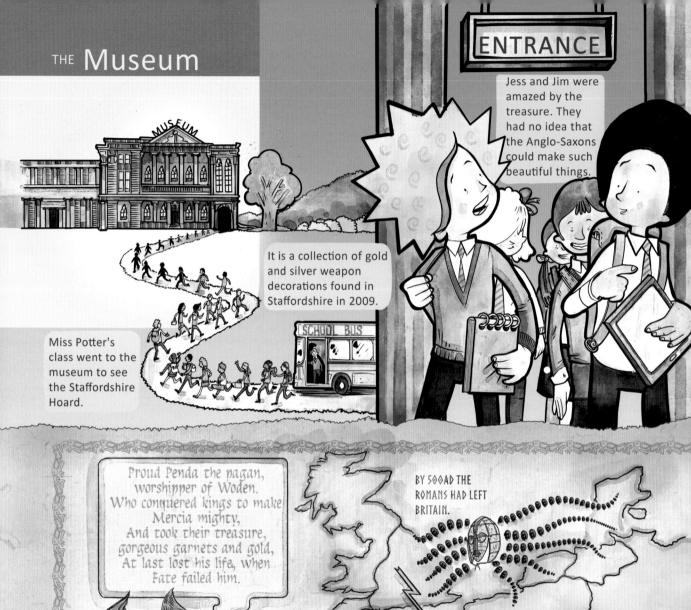

ENTRANCE

Jess and Jim were amazed by the treasure. They had no idea that the Anglo-Saxons could make such beautiful things.

It is a collection of gold and silver weapon decorations found in Staffordshire in 2009.

Miss Potter's class went to the museum to see the Staffordshire Hoard.

MUSEUM

SCHOOL BUS

Proud Penda the pagan,
worshipper of Woden.
Who conquered kings to make
Mercia mighty,
And took their treasure,
gorgeous garnets and gold,
At last lost his life, when
fate failed him.

BY 500AD THE ROMANS HAD LEFT BRITAIN.

IMMIGRANTS FROM GERMANY, DENMARK AND THE NETHERLANDS SETTLED IN ENGLAND.

Jess and Jim wanted to know more about the Staffordshire Hoard so that they could write an article for the school magazine. They asked Miss Potter for more information.

...so Jess and Jim decided to ask the experts!

But Miss Potter didn't seem to know very much...

THE ANGLO-SAXONS SPOKE THEIR OWN LANGUAGE AND WORSHIPPED THEIR OWN GODS.

WODEN WORHTE WEOS

IN THE MIDDLE OF ENGLAND KING PYBBA RULED OVER THE LITTLE KINGDOM OF MERCIA.

THE Finder

It's what metal-detectorists dream of.

a HoT SIGNAL!

When I asked the farmer to let me use my metal-detector on his field I thought I might find some old coins, but nothing like this!

SPLAT

BEEP BEEP

Remember, you are all children of the Royal House of Mercia, and the great god Woden is our ancestor.

PYBBA DIES.

What did you think you'd found?

At first I thought perhaps it was bits of an old jewellery box. Then I saw all the gold and the garnets and I thought, "It's an Anglo-Saxon hoard!" I was the first person to see it for nearly...

...1400 years!

There was too much of it. Gold was coming out of the ground like potatoes and the weather was terrible.

Did you dig it all up by yourself?

Birds like this were sacred to Woden, chief god of the Anglo-Saxons.

PENDA PLACES HIMSELF UNDER WODEN'S PROTECTION.

Mighty Woden, you must be my father now.

THE Archaeologist

Where was the Hoard found?

Where was it buried?

Archaeologists are like detectives. Things we find underground give us clues to how people lived in the past.

PENDA'S COUSIN CEORL SEIZES THE THRONE.

CEORL

CEORL'S DAUGHTER AND KING EDWIN OF NORTHUMBRIA ARE MARRIED.

Edwin, if you marry my daughter there will be peace between our kingdoms.

Brother, this marriage will just give the Northumbrians more power over us!

Why was it buried?

We don't know. It wasn't part of a burial. It wasn't very deep down.

So perhaps it was hidden by someone who meant to come back for it.

This eye-shaped piece, studded with garnets, may have decorated the cover of a book.

ANGLO-SAXON
ROMAN &
NEOLITHIC
PREHISTORIC

OLD ROMAN ROAD

It was on a hill overlooking an old Roman road. We dug it up carefully and kept records of what we found and where we found it. Sometimes where we find it and what we find it with gives us extra clues to what something might be.

PENDA AND HIS BROTHER PRACTISE THEIR FIGHTING SKILLS...

...AND PENDA PLAYS TAFL TO SHARPEN HIS WITS.

7

Metal-detectorists must contact us within two weeks when they find something that might be Treasure.

But what is Treasure?

PENDA AND HIS BROTHER OVERTHROW CEORL AND DECLARE INDEPENDENCE FROM NORTHUMBRIA. PENDA VOWS TO MAKE MERCIA POWERFUL.

By Woden's beard I shall not rest until Mercia is the most powerful kingdom in England.

KING CENWEALH of WESSEX

If it's more than three hundred years old and it's made of gold or silver: it's Treasure.

Experts decide how much they think it's worth, and the finder and the landowner share that money. Any museums that want it have to raise the money to buy it.

Before it was bent, this rich gold ornament showed two eagles holding a fish.

How did you feel when you first saw the Staffordshire Hoard?

All I could say was "Wow!" It's the biggest Anglo-Saxon treasure ever found.

I will marry your daughter and your son will marry my sister.

WESSEX

Our womenfolk shall be peace-weavers.

MERCIA

We will be friends forever.

Mighty Woden, I must win the respect and loyalty of my friends and foes.

Help me to build the greatest treasure hoard in England.

I'm an expert on Anglo-Saxon metalwork, so I was asked to make a catalogue: a list of everything in the Hoard, saying what we knew about it.

How did you keep count?

There were thousands of tiny pieces so I numbered everything with orange raffle tickets.

Sister, this is my good friend King Cadwallon of Wales. I'd like you to marry him.

But he's a Christian.

I have nothing against Christians as long as they keep their faith.

Did you know what everything was?

I knew most of the pieces were sword-hilt decorations because I'd seen similar things in other Anglo-Saxon finds.

This was the best that Anglo-Saxon metalworkers could do, and they were very good.

I didn't know what some of the other pieces were because I'd never seen anything like them, but I knew they were special.

Sword pyramids like this helped keep swords in their scabbards.

PENDA AND CADWALLON PLOT AGAINST THEIR ENEMIES.

Edwin of Northumbria is getting far too big for his boots. Let's teach him a lesson.

A chance to win more treasure for my hoard!

NORTHUMBRIA

POWYS

MERCIA

WESSEX

THE Conservator

About three-quarters of the Hoard is gold. Some pieces are decorated with gold wirework, or filigree. Some are silver. There are lots of garnets and a few bits of glass, and some fascinating gunk which fixed the garnets in place.

Is everything made of gold?

How did yo[u] clean them

CONSERVATOR'S TOOL BOX

THORN best tool to remove dirt

DISTILLED WATER

PIN VICE used fo[r] holding the thor[n]

CUTTING MAT a great surface for cleaning finds

PAINT BRUSH delicate particle removal

Notes

385

387

NOTE BOOK recording information

RAFFLE TICKET ROLL for labelling

TWEEZERS precision extraction tool

DISTILLED WATER softens dirt

STYROFOAM CASING used for protecting finds

RUBBER PUFF blows awa[y] dirt and dust

Some pieces were completely buried in lumps of earth. It was my job to clean the soil off them and to make sure they didn't fall to bits.

PENDA AND CADWALLON KILL EDWIN AT THE BATTLE OF HATFIELD CHASE.

Please don't kill me - I'm Edwin's son Eadfrith. We are kinsmen.

Gold is easily scratched. I had to clean it very gently, looking through a powerful microscope. I picked off the earth bit by bit with thorns because they're springy enough not to damage the gold.

When conservators cleaned this piece they found animal art: four eagles' heads.

You are growing powerful, Penda. A great lord needs a great hoard. I can turn blood-red garnets from India and ancient gold into the greatest treasure England has ever seen.

Your unswerving loyalty to Woden is all the payment I ask for. And you can call me Wayland.

Who are you? What must I pay you?

I swear by Woden's beard that I shall let no harm come to the hostage Eadfrith.

13

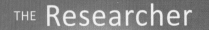

What's the most bits you've fitted together to make one piece?

This pommel cap from the end of a sword handle was broken into 26 bits. It's made of silver, decorated with gold wire, garnets, glass and white shell. When I fitted it together I realised it once had two silver rings fixed to it.

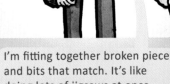

I'm fitting together broken pieces and bits that match. It's like doing lots of jigsaws at once.

Mercia must grow, and East Anglia is weak.

PENDA

SIGEBERHT

Sigeberht, leave your monastery and defend us against Penda.

I am a man of God. I will not bear a sword.

This staff is my weapon.

Is it solid gold?

It's mixed with small amounts of silver and copper. Gold-smiths treated it somehow to make the surfaces seem like pure gold.

KNOCK

DATA FEED

ELECTRONO 3000 ™

Silver

Gold

I'm analysing tiny specks of the gold to see what it can tell us about the Hoard.

WITH WAYLAND'S HELP, PENDA'S WEALTH AND POWER GROW.

You're the greatest goldsmith I've ever known. Your skill is almost like magic.

Who is this Oswald who has killed my friend Cadwallon?

He's the new Northumbrian king, sir. He's the most powerful man in England.

Only six Anglo-Saxon helmets have ever been found. This one is in lots of pieces. I'm trying to work out how it fitted together.

What did the helmet look like?

It was covered with rectangles of silver foil, stamped with pictures warriors. There was a gold horse' head above the nose.

6th Helmet

I have created a mighty helmet for you to wear into battle.

Oswald is attacking Mercia even though I did what he wanted.

We must stop him.

No! Not my brother!

Oswald will pay for this with his life!

This piece decorated with animal patterns is a cheekpiece.

It protected the side of your head.

Who wore a helmet like this?

It might have belonged to a king. When he wore his helmet he glittered in the sun like a god and inspired his warriors to fight to the death.

...ord have mercy on the souls of my warriors.

Woden will be pleased with this offering.

THE Swordsmith

I make copies of Anglo-Saxon sword blades, in the same way that they were made 1400 years ago.

What were Anglo-Saxon swords like?

PENDA ATTACKS THE NORTHUMBRIAN ROYAL FORTRESS

Sir, this is the finest battle-knife I have ever made.

I'll use it to fight Oswald's brother Oswy.

Bishop Aidan! Penda has set fire to my stronghold.

Behold, Lord, the great mischief Penda does.

Let's pray

THE Historian

The Hoard was buried in the kingdom of Mercia in pagan times. Pagan Anglo-Saxons didn't read or write, so most histories were written later by Christian monks. Although most Hoard objects are war-gear, some are Christian: crosses, and a gold strip engraved with a Bible quotation.

What have you found?

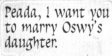

I'm finding out as much as I can about the Hoard from books and papers.

Peada, I want you to marry Oswy's daughter.

Cyneburgh, you must marry Oswy's son.

Will we have to become Christian?

PEADA

PENDA

CYNEBURGH

OSWY

PEADA CYNEBURGH OSWY'S SON OSWY'S DAUGHTER

Think of yourselves as peace-weavers.

This is written in Latin, the language of the Christian Church. It asks for God's help, probably in battle. It may be a clue to what its owner believed.

What did it say?

RISE UP O LORD & LET THOSE WHO HATE YOU FLEE BEFORE YOU & LET YOUR ENEMIES BE SCATTERED &

Your son's wife has brought Christian priests to Mercia.

Don't worry, Wayland. Woden knows I am loyal to him.

23

I plan exhibitions in my museum and tell visitors what they're about.

PLAN FOR MUSEUM

HELMET   MYSTERY   POTS   SHIELDS   SWORDS

GARNETS   BUCKLES   BOOK BITS

JEWELLERY

How do you choose what to display?

4000 BiTS ➜ **300 BiTS**

1. muddy
2. out
3. fragile
4. research
5. dirty
6. in microso...

broken
not stable
in a box
dusty
in bits

Although there are about 4,000 pieces of the Hoard only about 300 are big enough to display. have to choose bi that aren't being cleaned or researched, aren' too fragile, and aren't on show at other museums.

So the King of Wessex thinks he can just send my sister away when he's tired of her, does he?

THE KING OF WESSEX FLEES TO EAST ANGLIA.

Some amazing garnet cellwork pieces might be ornaments from a saddle, or from a book, or something else altogether.

THE Volunteer

I help at the museum, explaining the Hoard exhibition to visitors.

I try to answer visitors' questions. When the curators and researchers discover something new they tell me and then I tell the visitors.

What do you talk about?

One final battle with Northumbria for the glory of Woden!

We're hopelessly outnumbered.

If we give all our treasure to Penda perhaps he'll go away.

MERCIA

...RD WAS BURIED IN MERCIA BESIDE AN
ROAD 1400 YEARS AGO

COMPOSITION

It was made of precious gold, silver and garnets by England's finest craftsmen.

Most of the pieces are decorations from the handles of weapons.

TREASURE HOARD REVEALED

...his   might   have

CLEANING UP

Some of th...

EXPERTS BAFFLED BY MYSTERY

Even the experts don't know for certain who the treasure belonged to or why it was buried. They study history, archaeology and the Hoard itself, and make guesses based on the evidence they find.

LOOKING FOR CLUES

After archaeologists had carefully dug up the Hoard, they searched the field where it was found for clues to why it was buried there. They didn't find any graves or buildings, but the field was next to a Roman road, which was still used in Saxon times.

IMPRESSIVE WEAPONS

Experts think most Hoard pieces decorated the handles of magnificent swords or battle-knives. They dazzled friend and foe alike. Only wealthy and powerful warriors and commanders could...

STABILISE THE TREASURE

After archaeologists had carefully dug up the Hoard, they searched the field where it was found for clues to why it was buried there. They didn't find any graves or buildings, but the field was next to a Roman road, which was still used in Saxon times.

ANCIENT KINGDOM

In early Anglo-Saxon times England was made up of lots of different kingdoms ruled by rival kings. 1400 years ago Staffordshire, where the Hoard was found, was part of the Anglo-Saxon kingdom of Mercia. Mercian kings were warlike and power-hungry, and fought savage battles against neighbouring kings.

WHAT IS THE STORY OF THE STAFFORDSHIRE HOARD?

KIDS SPEAK TO THE REAL EXPERTS

After archaeologists had carefully dug up the Hoard, they searched the field where it was found for clues to why it was buried there. They didn't find any graves or buildings, but the field was next to a Roman road, which was still used in Saxon times.

Its owner must have been one of the most powerful men in England. Mercian kings were warlike and power-hungry, and fought savage battles against neighbouring kings.